ROBBIE WILLIAMS
REALITY KILLED THE VIDEO STAR

06. **MORNING SUN**

11. **BODIES**

17. **YOU KNOW ME**

22. **BLASPHEMY**

27. **DO YOU MIND**

32. **LAST DAYS OF DISCO**

38. **SOMEWHERE**

40. **DECEPATON**

44. **STARSTRUCK**

50. **DIFFICULT FOR WEIRDOS**

56. **SUPERBLIND**

62. **WON'T DO THAT**

66. **MORNING SUN REPRISE**

© 2009 by Faber Music Ltd. First published by Faber Music Ltd in 2009
Bloomsbury House 74–77 Great Russell Street, London WC1B 3DA

Arranged by Alex Davis
Edited by Lucy Holliday

Art direction and design: Tom Hingston Studio
Photography: Julian Broad

Printed in England by Caligraving Ltd
All rights reserved

The text paper used in this publication is a virgin fibre product that is manufactured
in the UK to ISO 14001 standards. The wood fibre used is only sourced from managed
forests using sustainable forestry principles. This paper is 100% recyclable.

ISBN10: 0-571-53420-1
EAN13: 978-0-571-53420-3

Reproducing this music in any form is illegal and forbidden by the Copyright,
Designs and Patents Act, 1988.

To buy Faber Music publications or to find out about the full range of titles available,
please contact your local music retailer or Faber Music sales enquiries:
Faber Music Ltd, Burnt Mill, Elizabeth Way, Harlow, CM20 2HX England
Tel: +44 (0) 1279 82 89 82   Fax: +44 (0) 1279 82 89 83
sales@fabermusic.com
fabermusic.com

MORNING SUN

Words and Music by Robbie Williams, Danny Spencer,
Kelvin Andrews, Scott Ralph, Richard Scott and Don Black

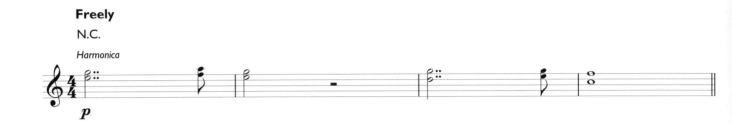

sat there ev- 'ry morn - ing, and watched the sun rise?__

BODIES

Words and Music by Robbie Williams, Craig Russo and Brandon Christy

- tion.

1. F#m7

2. F#m7

(vocals)

Yeah!

_mf_

_mp_

F#m

Bo-dies in the bo-dhi tree,___ bo-dies ma-king che-mis-try, bo-dies on my fa-mi-ly,

_mf_

YOU KNOW ME

Words and Music by Robbie Williams, Danny Spencer and Kelvin Andrews

BLASPHEMY

Words and Music by Robbie Williams and Guy Chambers

1. The E-gyp - tians built their py - ra - mids, the Ro - mans did what they did, now

2. (Words cut) like a knife through Va - se - line, you can't real - ly mean what you mean

ev - 'ry - thing's come down to this, it's just you and I our kid. We

when you say what you say, tou - rettes make them come out that way. Wish

1.   I can't be-have.   I know it's not the hea - then in___ me, it's
2.   I can't be-have.   No it's not the hea - then in___ me, it's
𝄋.   I can't be-have.   I know it's not the hea - then in___ me, it's

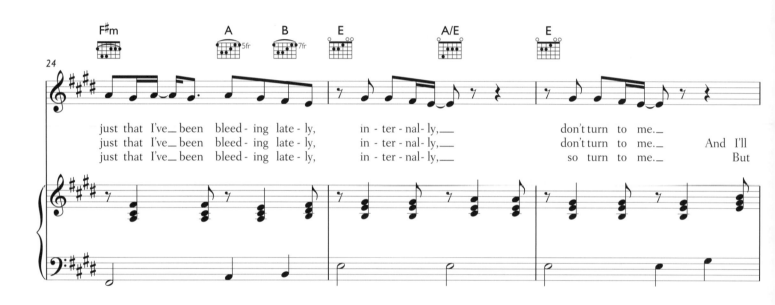

just that I've_been bleed-ing late-ly,   in - ter-nal-ly,__   don't turn to me._
just that I've_been bleed-ing late-ly,   in - ter-nal-ly,__   don't turn to me._   And I'll
just that I've_been bleed-ing late-ly,   in - ter-nal-ly,__   so turn to me._   But

Bite your tongue, the tor-rid wea-pon,   you could learn a use-ful les-son.
bite my tongue, the tor-rid wea-pon,   I could learn a use-ful les-son.
bite your tongue, your tor-rid wea-pon,   we could learn a use-ful les-son. }   What's so great a-bout the

⊕ Coda

Ain't it great, this great de-pres-sion? It's not a blast for me,

it's blas-phe - my.___

DO YOU MIND

Words and Music by Robbie Williams,
Danny Spencer, Kelvin Andrews and Charles Jankel

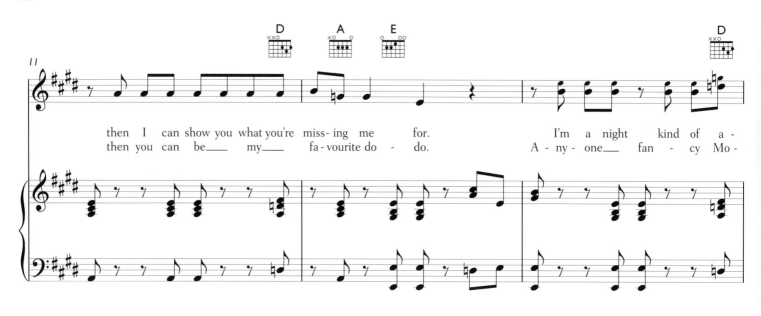

then I can show you what you're miss-ing me for.
then you can be__ my__ fa-vourite do - do.
I'm a night kind of a-
A - ny-one__ fan-cy Mo-

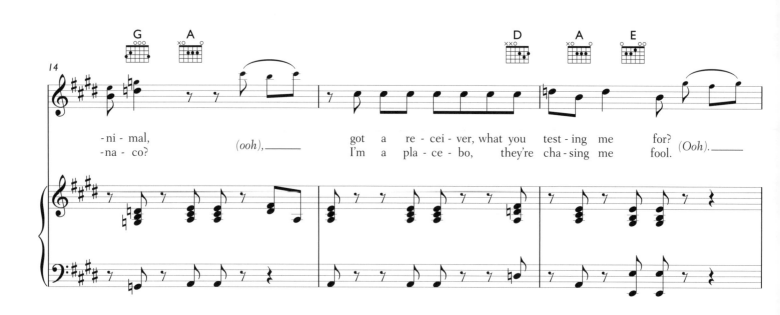

-ni - mal,
-na - co?
(ooh),__
got a re-cei-ver, what you test-ing me for? (Ooh).__
I'm a pla-ce-bo, they're cha-sing me fool. (Ooh).__

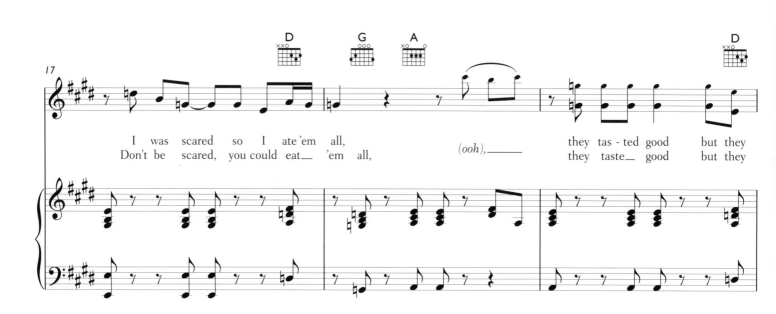

I was scared so I ate 'em all,
Don't be scared, you could eat__ 'em all,
(ooh),__
they tas-ted good but they
they taste__ good but they

LAST DAYS OF DISCO

Words and Music by Robbie Williams, Danny Spencer and Kelvin Andrews

1. Stand by me, I've been stood by you for a - ges.
2. All raved out, bit - ter is the pill of de - vo - tion.

Stay calm and car - ry on, may - be no - thing's wrong.
Read be - tween the noise, all you dis - co boys.

Is it the com-fort of, dis-in-for-ma-tion, or is it the free-dom that you fear?
The fa-sci-na-tion of, a boy and girl in love, for a se-cond I can see her,

Said I'm the an-gel of li-be-ra-tion, love, for a se-cond I be-lieve her.
in the mir-ror-ball, the hu-man a-ni-mal I'm the crea-ture that I fear.

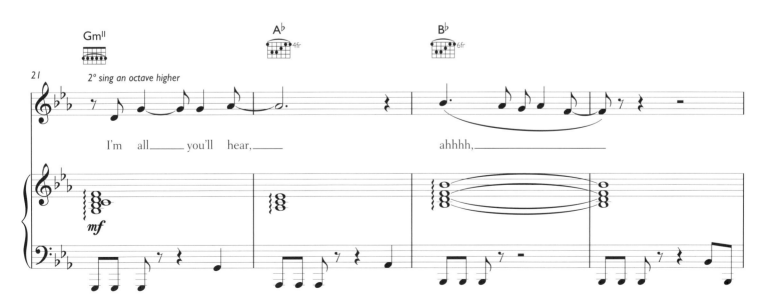

2° sing an octave higher

I'm all you'll hear, ahhhh,

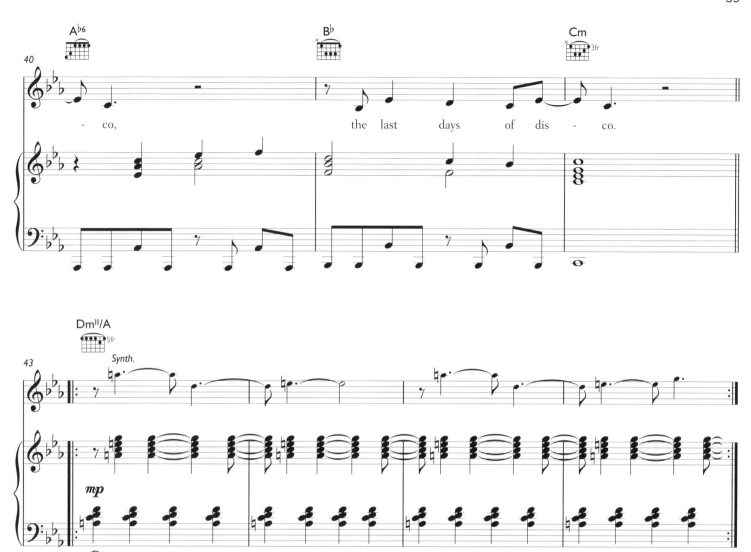

-co, the last days of dis - co.

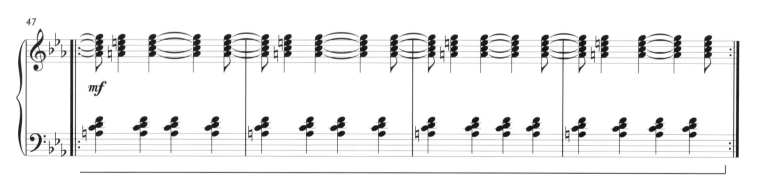

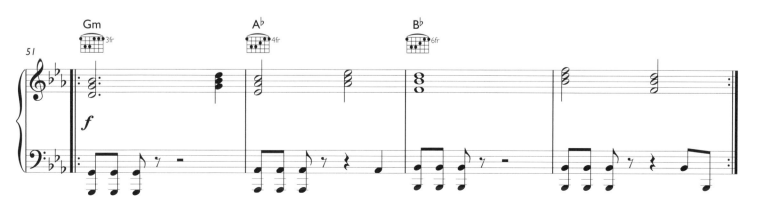

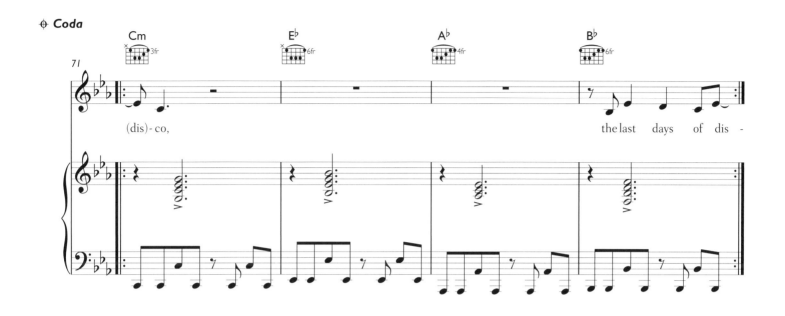

(dis)-co,   the last days of dis -

- co.

SOMEWHERE

Words and Music by Danny Spencer, Kelvin Andrews,
Andrew Stubbs, Stephen Cadman and Jonathan Hand

DECEPTACON

Words and Music by Robbie Williams, Danny Spencer,
Kelvin Andrews, Scott Ralph and Richard Scott

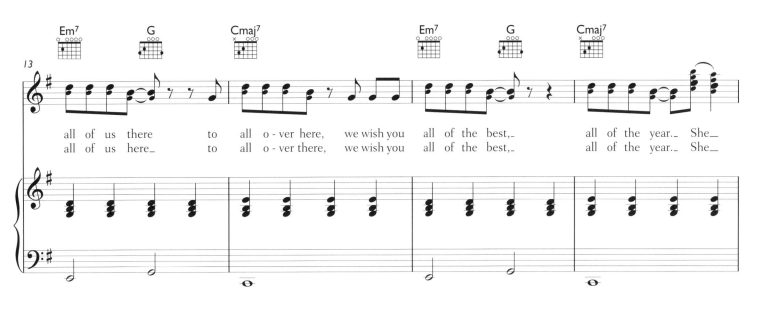

all of us there__ to all o-ver here, we wish you all of the best,__ all of the year.__ She__
all of us here__ to all o-ver there, we wish you all of the best,__ all of the year.__ She__

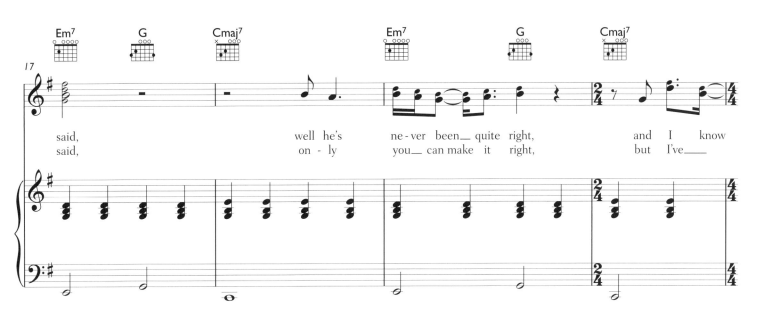

said, well he's ne-ver been__ quite right, and I know
said, on-ly you__ can make it right, but I've__

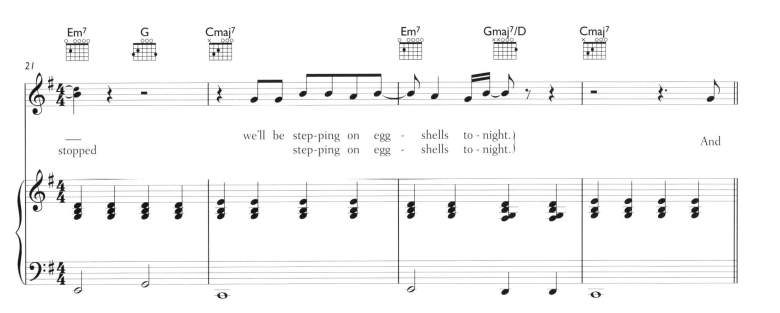

__ we'll be step-ping on egg - shells to-night.)
stopped step-ping on egg - shells to-night.)

And

STARSTRUCK

Words and Music by Robbie Williams,
Danny Spencer, Kelvin Andrews and Paul Beard

Rea- dy, stea- dy, go.

Ooh..._____

DIFFICULT FOR WEIRDOS

Words and Music by Robbie Williams, Danny Spencer and Kelvin Andrews

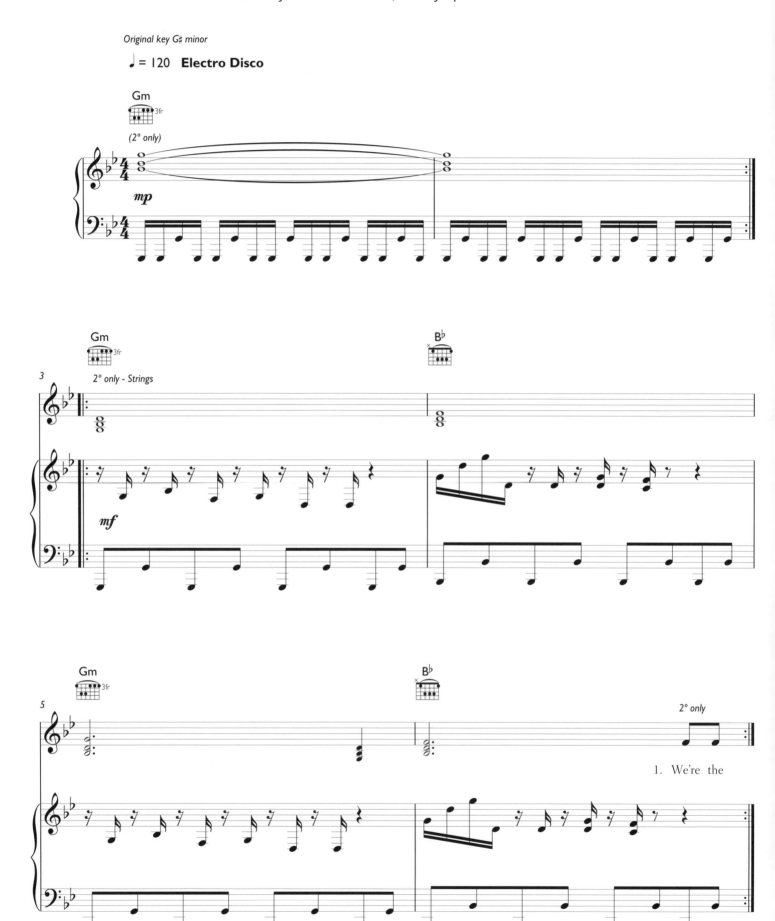

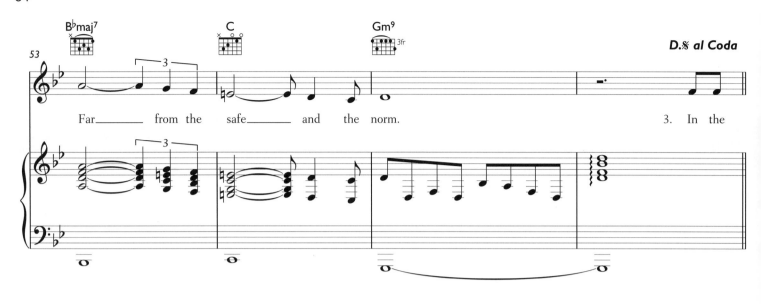

D.% al Coda

Far_____ from the safe_____ and the norm.

3. In the

Coda

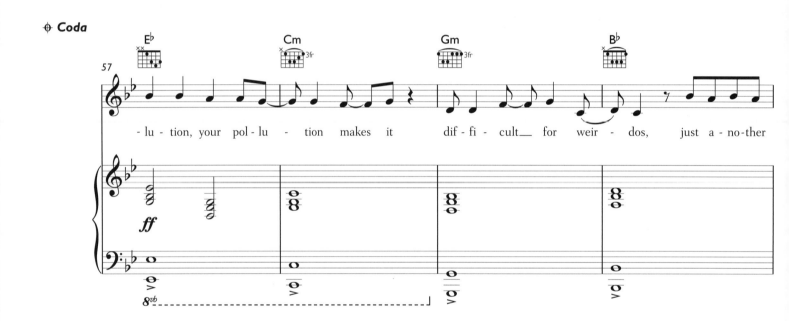

-lu - tion, your pol-lu - tion makes it dif-fi-cult___ for weir-dos, just a-no-ther

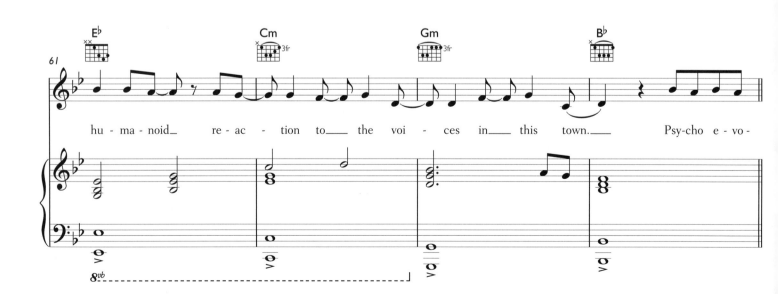

hu - ma-noid___ re - ac - tion to___ the voi - ces in___ this town.___ Psy-cho e-vo-

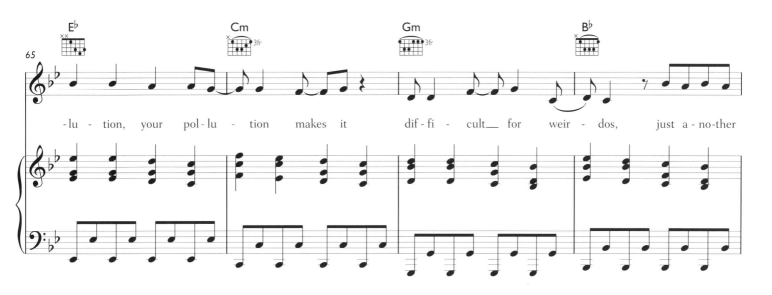

-lu - tion, your pol-lu - tion makes it dif-fi - cult___ for weird - os, just a-no-ther

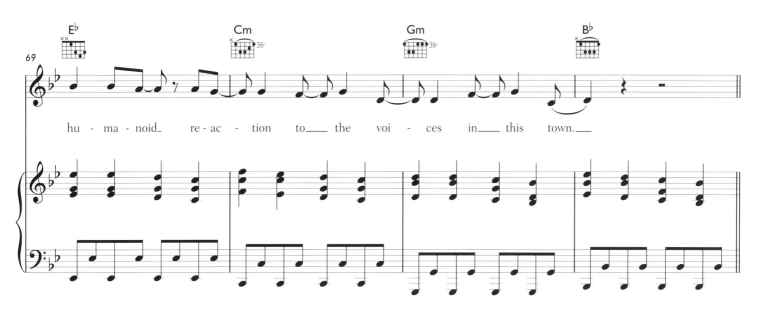

hu - ma - noid___ re - ac - tion to___ the voi - ces in___ this town.___

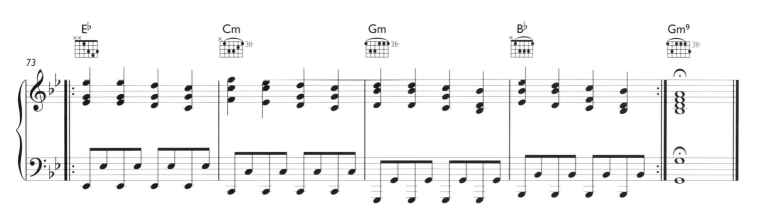

SUPERBLIND

Words and Music by Robbie Williams and Fil Eisler

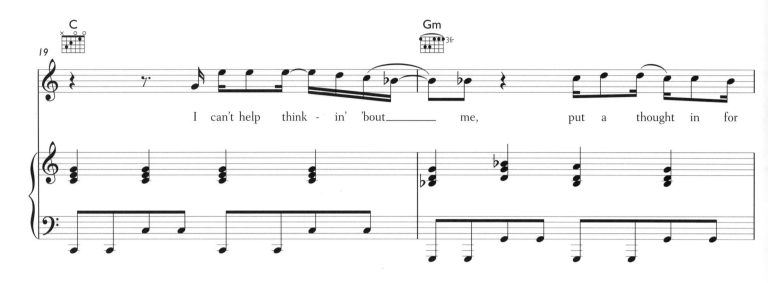

I can't help think - in' 'bout_____ me, put a thought in for

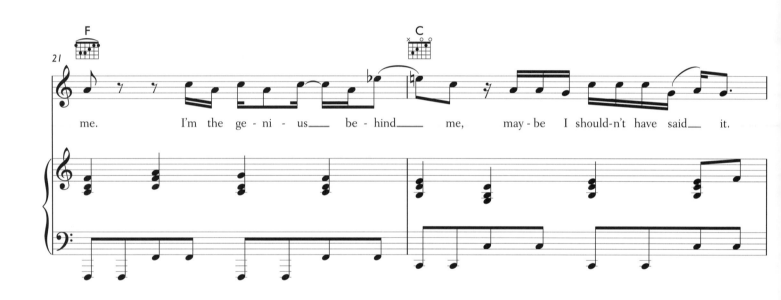

me. I'm the ge - ni - us_____ be - hind_____ me, may - be I should - n't have said_____ it.

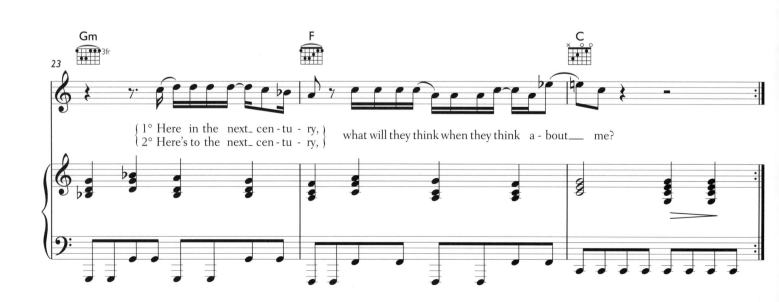

{1° Here in the next_ cen - tu - ry,}
{2° Here's to the next_ cen - tu - ry,} what will they think when they think a - bout_____ me?

we can pray___ our way___ out___ of this.

You're like a new___ wave old___ ro- man - tic,

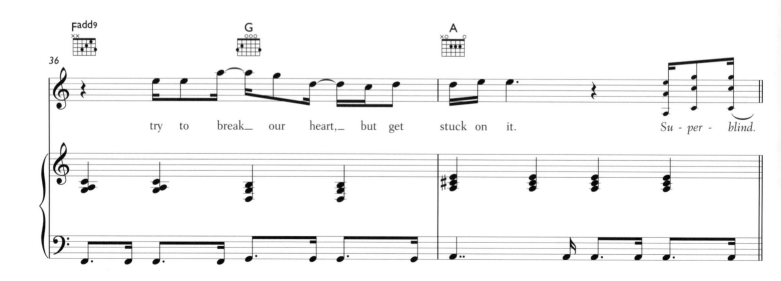

try to break___ our heart,___ but get stuck on it.　*Su - per - blind.*

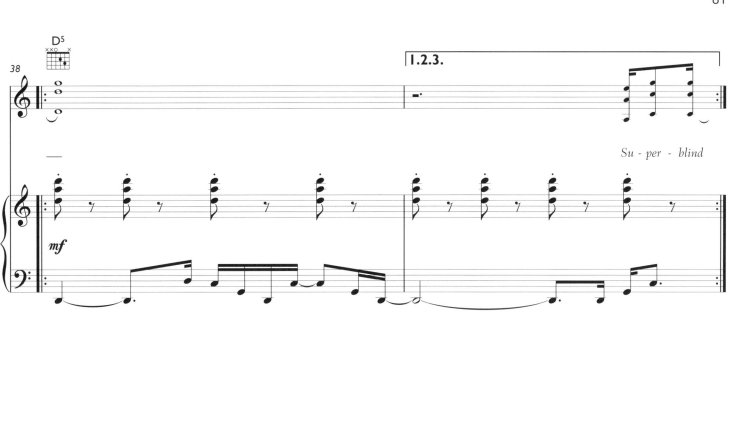

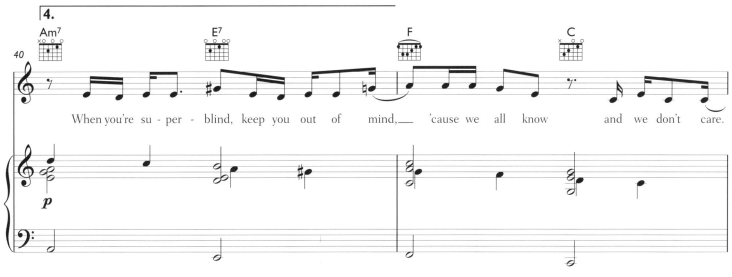

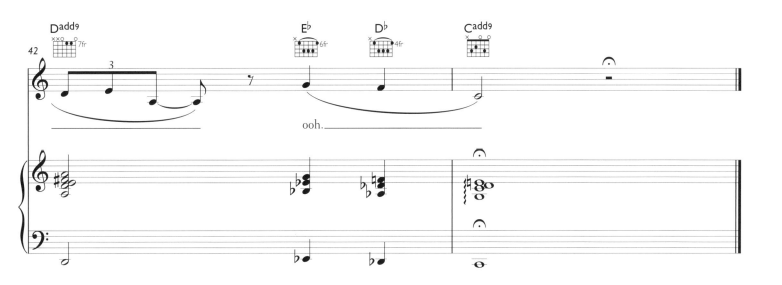

WON'T DO THAT

Words and Music by Robbie Williams, Danny Spencer,
Kelvin Andrews, Scott Ralph and Richard Scott

Sud-den-ly I'm not the jea-lous guy,__ a-no-ther sign__ that we're do-ing it right.

I could give this up, I could walk a-way, 'cause you fill me up each and ev-'ry day.__

MORNING SUN REPRISE

Words and Music by Robbie Williams, Danny Spencer,
Kelvin Andrews, Scott Ralph, Richard Scott and Don Black

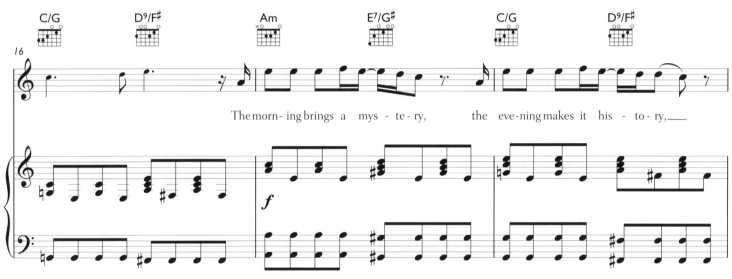

The morn-ing brings a mys-te-ry, the eve-ning makes it his-to-ry,___

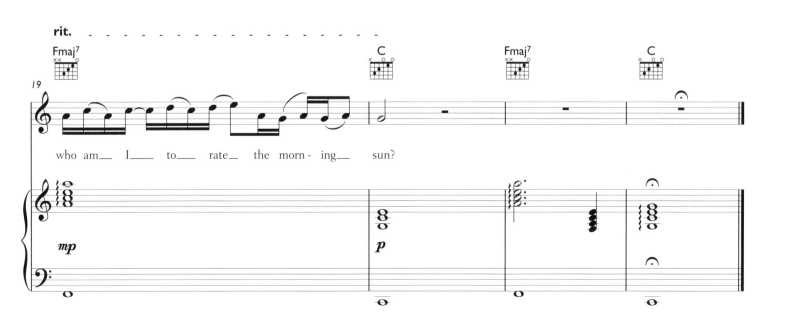

who am___ I___ to___ rate___ the morn-ing___ sun?